THE SLEEP BOOK

Teaching your child (9 months+) to sleep through the night

Kathy Macdonald/Leslie Centre

Illustrations by Clive Stone

REED

Published by Reed Books, a division of Reed Publishing (NZ)
Ltd, 39 Rawene Road, Birkenhead, Auckland. Associated
companies, branches and representatives throughout the world.

ISBN 0 7900 0030 X

First published 1985
Reprinted 1986, 1988, 1989, 1990, 1992

Design by Paper Dart, Auckland
Printed by Kim Hup Lee Printing Co. Ltd., Singapore

CONTENTS

When your child won't sleep

From ghoulies and ghosties,
And long-leggety beasties,
And kids that won't sleep in the night,
May the Good Lord deliver us.
    Variation on a Cornish folk verse

Can night-time become a nightmare in your household?

Do you have a child who is difficult to get to bed and impossible to keep there — maybe a nine-month-old who cries in the cot for no apparent reason but is all smiles as soon as you appear at the door? Perhaps you have a three-year-old who refuses to go to bed and likes to come and join you in the middle of the night? Does your little angel — who is much loved and in most respects normal and well behaved by day — sometimes seem more like a demon at night?

One of the most common problems for young children and their parents is lack of sleep. Tired, grizzly children and tired, irritable parents; battles over bedtime, and households disturbed by heart-rending cries or perhaps the pitter-patter of little feet in the early hours of the morning — no matter how it happens in your family, if your child is not getting enough sleep, then the chances are that both parents and child have a problem.

Difficulties with sleep concern parents of young children more than any other problem. That's not surprising when you consider that more than a quarter of all one- to two-year-olds wake most nights. It's a problem that concerns the whole household because it affects the child's daytime behaviour, it affects other children in the family — and it leaves parents lacking in energy for their children and themselves.

Of course all children will wake in the night sometimes. We are

1

not talking about the parent who has to deal with the occasional disturbed sleep or who sometimes has to care for a sick child during the night. This is part of the job of being a parent and most parents expect it. When you know that there's a good reason for your child's waking, you can understand it and you care for them as patiently as possible. When it happens only occasionally, you can tolerate it and expect to catch up on your sleep the next night.

This book is for the other parents, the large number whose children have difficulties with sleep almost every night. These difficulties include trouble getting children to bed, waking in the night and all the consequences of this — for the child and for the rest of the family.

What do the parents say?

The best people to describe sleep problems are the parents who have experienced them first-hand. Hundreds of parents have written or spoken to us about their difficulties with children's sleep and the effects on their households. Perhaps you will recognise some of the situations described by these parents:

The problems begin at bedtime...

- *Jerry is a delightful child until bedtime, then the nightmare begins.*
- *The difficulty in settling her upsets me more than the night-waking. I get desperately tired and have no evening to call my own ever.*
- *Getting my child to sleep at night begins at 7 o'clock and can take anything up to 10.30 or 11 o'clock, by which time I am utterly exhausted.*

... and continue through the night.

- *He is reluctant to go back to sleep in the night by himself, and it usually takes an emotional scene before he is settled. No matter how angry I am, he still wakes up the following night.*
- *Waking up begins about 11 p.m. and continues through the night. If we leave her, she cries; if we bring her into our bed, she wriggles and we don't get to sleep anyway.*
- *On a good night he wakes only two times.*

Lack of sleep can have a serious effect on daytime behaviour. Tired children may be grizzly, irritable or over-active. They may be 'hyped-up' from lack of sleep at night and refuse to sleep during the day.

- *When she doesn't sleep well, she is grizzling and clingy right from the start of the day. She won't eat properly and nothing pleases her. She looks very tired and still refuses to sleep.*
- *Moana needs more sleep as she is whining and cross through the day and most unpleasant to be with.*
- *He is very active all day and seldom has a sleep, although he does look tired.*

When children do not learn to sleep by themselves at night, they will often not separate from their parents during the day.

- *My child is clingy when people visit and it is quite impossible for me to leave him with anyone else because he cries and screams just like he does at night-time.*

The effects of sleep problems on parents include tiredness and exhaustion.

- *I am so exhausted I can't cope with anything else. Household chores get left undone almost every day because she is grizzly from lack of sleep.*
- *The lack of sleep is wearing me down physically and mentally.*
- *I am at my wits' end trying to cope with it all but I'm not succeeding.*

Many parents have done everything they can think of to solve the problem and now feel helpless and resigned.

- *My husband and I get so that we are giddy and exhausted to put it mildly! We've resigned ourselves to the fact that one day they will come right, and in the meantime we hope and pray that we'll be given the necessary strength to cope.*
- *I really feel that I've tried everything and just don't know what to do any more.*
- *We have tried nearly everything — cot in our room, a bottle, a night light, even medication from the doctor — but nothing seems to work.*

Feelings of anger and resentment towards the child are common, and it is possible for the relationship between parent and child to suffer.

- *We are feeling pretty desperate at this stage, as Bill goes off to work each day feeling quite had it and I get up in the morning feeling*

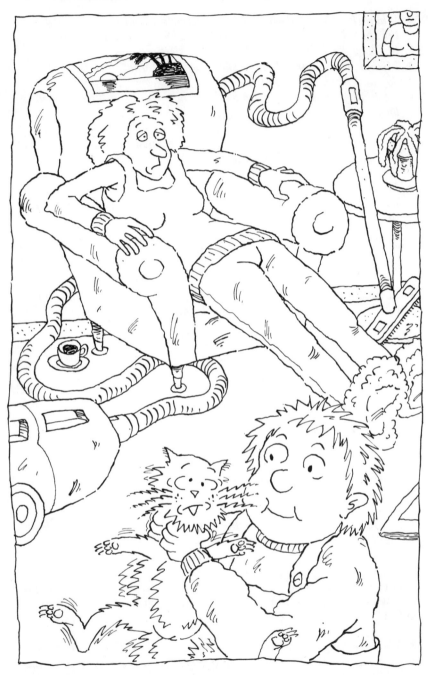

The effects of sleep problems on parents include tiredness and exhaustion.

quite exhausted — and sometimes feel quite bad-tempered with her because of it.
- *There has been many a night when we've felt the urge to bash them just to get them to stop crying.*
- *My husband and I both feel stretched to the limit and find we are disliking Jason more and more.*
- *I feel that I never have a moment to call my own. It feels like I am at his beck and call twenty-four hours a day and I'm starting to resent that.*

Sleep problems may seriously affect the time parents have for themselves and for their relationships with other adults.

- *I have never been able to leave my daughter overnight with my parents or any relatives because she does not sleep... I don't go out often.*
- *David often doesn't go to bed until 9.30 p.m., and I find I have no time to myself and I am constantly tired and scratchy.*
- *My wife and I are so exhausted that it takes a lot of effort to do everything.*
- *We find that we have no time to enjoy each other's company because all our time is spent with our daughter.*

The problem may affect all family members and all parts of family life.

- *I am sure that the nightly conflict was very damaging to all family relationships. It was certainly undermining my self-confidence.*
- *I get so angry because I'm forever up every night... but my problems are real and I want so much to be calm and happy with both my children and to have a contented pregnancy.*
- *Our whole family was suffering because of one member. Not only was Kelly irritable and hard to live with, but since I wasn't getting enough sleep, I didn't have the energy I needed to give to the other children.*

To conclude: Sleep problems in young children are common and they can be serious for all concerned. Many people find that things tend to get worse as time goes by. Parents tend to get more tired and run down, children get more difficult to manage, parents start to resent their children more, and interactions between parent and child tend to focus more and more on things that are wrong rather than on enjoying each other. It's like a snowball rolling downhill, gradually getting bigger and more out of control.

For other people, the problem does not seem so serious and there's no urgency to do anything about it. Only you can know how serious it is in your family and only you can decide whether you want to do something about it. Before you decide, there's an important fact you need to know about your child's sleep problem — you can change it! And it's worth considering some of the benefits you could expect if you were all getting a good night's sleep. Let's hear the good news about sleep problems and look at some of the success stories from people who have taught their children to sleep through the night.

When your child does sleep

It is the most wonderful feeling in the world to at last feel rested and to no longer feel the chronic fatigue of endless broken nights' sleep.

It is a joy to have Caroline so happy and settled with her daily routine, for me to be feeling so relaxed, rested and well, and for my husband no longer to go to work bleary eyed and oh so tired!

The good news

The good news about your child's sleep problem is that you don't have to put up with it. You can change it, and you can change it just as you are already changing lots of their behaviour — by using your adult wisdom and experience to teach the many skills needed for growing up.

Learning to sleep through the night is an important part of growing up, just like learning to walk, talk and being toilet-trained. It is a whole new skill, which some children seem to learn automatically, but others need more help with — just as some children seem to toilet-train themselves easily but others need lots of help and encouragement from their parents. When your child first learns to sleep regularly through the night, this is a basic step away from babyhood — and an important step in their development.

Some children learn to sleep through the night at an early age but later begin waking again. This sometimes happens after an illness, or when there has been a disruption to the usual routine. When you teach these children to sleep through the night again, you are helping them to give up a bad habit and are putting them back on the path towards growing up.

Perhaps your child has never learned to sleep through the night or perhaps they have abandoned their good sleep patterns after some disruption to the routine. Either way, the changes will be enormous when they are settling happily at bedtime and sleeping through

7

the night in their own bed. You will notice a difference in their behaviour, in the way you feel, and in the whole family atmosphere.

Once again, we'll let the parents explain

Parents report that the benefits of sleep begin with the way children feel about bed. Bedtime becomes a happy time — as it should be.

- *Since doing the programme, she has begun to love her bed. When nap time arrives, it is a real struggle to change her nappies, because all she wants to do is to get in her cot ... wonderful!*
- *Sleep is now either instant or he will play for a while and then put himself to bed. There is never any crying when he is taken to bed, which is beautiful. He is just so happy about his sleeping that often I will find him in bed in the afternoon sound asleep.*
- *How nice it is not to get that awful sinking feeling in your stomach as bedtime approaches.*

And children are happier when they wake up in the morning.

- *Our little daughter now wakes up in a happy frame of mind, whereas before she would wake up very tired and scratchy after a bad night.*
- *Michael is like a different child now that he's getting a good night's sleep. He plays happily in his room when he first wakes up, and he's much brighter and easier to manage right from the beginning.*

Often there are noticeable improvements in daytime behaviour because children are getting enough sleep, their parents are pleased with them, and the children feel proud of their success.

- *He is going terrific, sleeping through the night and a nap during the day. He is much easier to handle during the day. My parents came to stay and couldn't get over the change in him. His personality is better.*
- *As far as my little girl is concerned, I would say she has developed a great deal more confidence in herself and her ability to cope with situations.*
- *We are so happy, and our little girl is a different child now she is no longer over-tired.*

Parents can also get a decent night's sleep. This helps them to be more patient and caring during the day and often to enjoy a better relationship with their child.

- *I find that I'm a much nicer mother now that I'm not so tired. And I really look forward to seeing Robert in the morning, instead of dreading another day.*
- *I was getting tired of being constantly tired, but I feel so much better now with unbroken sleep and can enjoy Lucy even more than before.*
- *Looking back, I don't know how I coped. It's such a relief to be sleeping well now and to have so much more energy. I'm feeling much better about myself and about Vicki than I have for a long time.*

And at last parents can begin to do some of the things they want to do for themselves and for their relationships with adults and other children.

- *The difference in our life-style is astounding. My husband and I can enjoy peaceful evenings together, we can have people for dinner, I can read books again. I am far less tired and a great deal more fun for my daughter to live with.*
- *I feel we have a happier family and not a tired one dominated by a problem sleeper.*
- *I now have more time to spend with my older children in the evenings, I can go out again because I can use babysitters and, most of all, I'm feeling like 'me' and not just 'mother'. I had begun to forget who 'I' was!*
- *Knowing I have an hour during the day when I can guarantee he'll sleep is an absolute boon. I can rest or get the sort of things done that I simply cannot manage with a pre-schooler underfoot.*

Age, stage and sleep

How much sleep does your child need?

The amount of sleep children need will depend on their age and will vary a bit from child to child. At first glance, some children don't seem to need much sleep at all. They can be awake half the night and on the go all day, while exhausted parents wonder where they get the energy from. Some young children will refuse a daytime sleep and still argue that they are not tired at bedtime. But don't be fooled! They may be getting much less sleep than they need and be over-active as a result.

Many parents are amazed to discover that, once their child has learned to sleep through the night, their child is more relaxed and able to sleep longer than ever before. They may not only sleep longer at night, but may add a daytime sleep as well — just when the parents thought this was no longer necessary.

Children do not have the wisdom to know how much sleep they need. If you let them decide what time to go to bed and how much sleep to have, they may get what they want but not what they need. As a parent, you make lots of decisions about what is best for your child and your decisions are not always popular. You don't usually let them decide whether to have chocolates instead of vegetables for dinner, whether to go out in the cold without a jersey, or whether to play on the road. Similarly, *you* have to decide how much sleep your child needs. Here are some guidelines:

Birth to three months
Of course, you don't expect a new-born baby to sleep through the night. They are likely to wake every few hours and need feeding, changing, and lots of smiles and cuddles.

They also spend lots of time asleep — up to twenty hours a day — but are not yet capable of sleeping for too long without a feed. And if they're hungry, they usually let you know in no uncertain terms. So naturally, you attend to a young baby who cries because that's their way of telling you they need something.

10

Three to nine months
Ideally, children of this age will be sleeping longer without needing a feed — and by nine months most children are capable of sleeping through the night. Some children will learn to sleep through well before they are nine months old — and will continue to do so through teething, house-moving and any number of visits to distant relatives. Others are not so lucky.

In general, you can expect a child between three and nine months to sleep twelve to fourteen hours out of every twenty-four. Ideally, this will be divided between long blocks of sleep through the night and two daytime sleeps as well. A routine like this will make your life easier to organise and will also be good for your baby. It gives them the sleep they need and allows you time to sleep and time to get on with your chores. This is not selfish but good common sense — good for baby and good for parents. If a parent is not well rested and able to cope, the whole family suffers.

Nine months
As long as your child is healthy, and you are sure in your own mind that they don't need a feed in the middle of the night, you can expect your nine-month-old to sleep through the night.

How can you be sure your child is ready?
First of all you must be sure that your child is healthy. Sick children may need attention through the night, and the best sleepers can be disturbed by pain. Sometimes children don't sleep because they have an undiagnosed medical problem such as an ear infection or an allergic reaction to food. If you are in any doubt at all, have your child checked by a doctor.

The next important sign that your child is ready to sleep through is that they no longer need feeding in the night. It's not easy to sleep when you are hungry. If your baby is gaining weight and settling into a routine of three or four main meals a day, then it's likely they're not hungry in the night. And if the baby demands a feed in the night but then takes only a few sucks and wants to play, they're giving you another clue that hunger is not the problem.

Finally, take a look at how much your baby has changed since birth. By nine months they're already very different from a little newborn. They're starting to recognise that there are people other than Mum or Dad who can be trusted. They'll be amusing themselves for short periods of time and will be more mobile. When they cry in the night they may grin broadly as soon as you appear — and you know that they're having you on! When you go in your child may insist that they want someone else. These are clear examples of the difference between what is wanted and what is needed. These are signs that your child is getting older and is now capable of sleeping through the night — although they may prefer not to.

At nine months you can expect your child to sleep twelve to fourteen hours a day. They will be making a transition in the next few months from a morning and an afternoon sleep to one long middle-of-the-day sleep. From now on, the decision on when to sleep and how much is up to you. Remember, the amount of sleep they get when they decide for themselves may not be as much as they need.

Two years and on

Both you and your two-year-old need a good night's sleep. Your child is probably on the go all day, with you struggling hard to keep up. It is likely that they still need twelve to fourteen hours sleep a day. And you? ... Well, as the parent of a two-year-old, you also have a busy life and need plenty of sleep to keep you going.

It is important for both of you that your child has a daytime sleep or rest. Just how much sleep a two-year-old needs during the day varies from child to child and depends on how long they sleep at night. Some children might need two to three hours, others much less. Some need a sleep daily, others only every second day. However, whether they sleep or not, both you and your child will benefit from the routine of a daily rest.

There's no need to explain how valuable a break is for you during the day — for resting or for getting things done without a child around. And it's really good for your child to have a daily quiet time, even if they don't always get to sleep. They can use the time to rest, to learn to be alone, and to play quietly. It can be a time when your child slows down from the day's hectic activities and, above all, it can be a time to enjoy.

Sounds impossible? ... Then read on.

Decide what you want for your family

So now you know how much sleep you can expect your child to have — and you know they're not getting enough. Or else they're getting enough sleep but only after finally deciding to settle at 11.00 p.m. Or maybe they sleep beautifully — but only in your bed, with you getting kicked and pushed about all night and perhaps stumbling off to find somewhere else to sleep.

This doesn't mean you have a problem. It's only a problem if it's not what you want for your child, yourself and your family. You are the expert on your child and only you can decide what is right for your family.

One of the first decisions you make will be about whether your child really needs you when they wake at night or whether waking is just a habit. If you decide that they need you, naturally you will attend to them and find ways of helping your family cope with the general lack of sleep — perhaps by calling on more support from others, by finding ways of giving yourself a break during the day, or by scaling down unnecessary activities. You've only got a problem if you decide that your child doesn't really need you and that it's not in their interests — or yours — to continue having nights of broken sleep.

Another basic decision is about whether you want an adult bed or a family bed where everyone piles in and stays. There's no problem if you and your child are happy sleeping in the same bed. It's only a problem if you decide that you want an adult bed and that you want your child to learn to sleep alone.

If you have decided that you want an adult bed and not a family bed, and that your child does not really need you every time they wake, you may still not be ready to teach them to sleep through the night. There are some other decisions you have to make first about what you want for your family.

13

There's no problem if you and your child are happy sleeping in the same bed. It's only a problem if you decide that you want an adult bed and that you want your child to sleep alone.

Do you want:

1.	A child who doesn't like their bed	or	A child who enjoys being in bed
2.	Battles over bedtime	or	A child who goes to bed happily
3.	A child who needs medication to get to sleep	or	A child who goes to sleep naturally
4.	A child who can only go to sleep with a parent present	or	A child who can drift off to sleep alone
5.	Evening time with children around	or	Evening time to call your own
6.	A child who wakes in the night through habit and cries to get your attention	or	Waking and crying during the night only when there's something really wrong
7.	Broken nights, small night visitors, musical beds	or	An uninterrupted night's sleep
8.	A little figure who appears at your bedside at 4.30 a.m. shouting, 'The sun's up'	or	A child who stays in their room until they hear the signal for getting-up time
9.	A tired, grizzly child who is unable to enjoy family activities	or	A happy, relaxed child who is able to enjoy the exciting things each day has to offer
10.	A tired, grizzly parent during the day	or	A parent with enough energy to cope with day-to-day living, and with some energy left over to enjoy themselves
11.	A child who's not quite sure what's expected	or	A child who has the security of clear rules
12.	A child who is the most powerful person in the household	or	A child who knows that the parents are in charge

Remember, you are the expert on your family and only you can decide what you want. If you have made the second choice in all these decisions, this book will show you how to get what you want.

Myths can be blinding and paralysing

What can you believe?

Have you noticed that one of the joys of being a parent is that everyone else is an expert on your child — and all the experts disagree! There's no shortage of advice given about sleep problems, and it's sometimes hard to know what to believe when you are confused by conflicting advice — and perhaps so tired that it's hard to think clearly anyway. It might help you to sort out the advice you've been given if we look at some of the more popular myths you may have heard about sleep.

Many parents are stuck with a sleep problem because they are victims of myths about their children's sleep. Myths can stop you seeing the problem as it is and can stop you doing something effective to change it. These myths lead to parents feeling defeated and children feeling wide awake.

Below are listed some of the more common myths, with brief comments about them:

Myth: 'It's a stage' or 'My child will grow out of it'
As we have already discussed, most children have by nine months reached the stage of being capable of sleeping through the night. If the not-sleeping stage has gone on beyond nine months, then it's gone on for too long. Parents who wait for their children to 'grow out of it' may be waiting unnecessarily for something they could teach their child to do almost immediately. And they may be waiting for a long time. It's not uncommon for children of three or four to continue having problems sleeping through the night. In fact, surveys have found that fourteen per cent of three-year-olds still wake regularly at night.

If you wait for your child to 'grow out of it', you are letting them decide when to sleep and how much sleep to have. Your child may not have the wisdom to make these decisions — just as they may

17

Have you noticed that one of the joys of being a parent is that everyone else is an expert on your child — and all the experts disagree!

lack the wisdom to know not to play with the carving knife. This is an area where guidance is needed from a caring adult who has the child's best interests at heart.

Myth: 'My child needs me at 2 a.m.'

Needs you for what? For reassurance that you're there and that you care? Why should they doubt it? During the day you give your child lots of love and attention, and do your best to meet their needs. At night you can put them to bed confident that what is most needed is a good night's sleep. However, if you think some kind of reassurance is warranted, you could make some clear statements at bedtime, explaining where you will be spending the rest of the evening, where you will be sleeping and when you will be available in the morning.

If your child is waking every night, it is likely to be from habit rather than because they really need something. And remember that your needs are important too — you need a good night's sleep so you have plenty of energy for yourself and for your child the next day.

Myth: 'My child suffers from bad dreams'

Bad dreams are likely to occur only occasionally with most young children. You can usually tell when your child has had a nightmare by the suddenness of the waking — and by the signs of real fear in their crying and perhaps in their body trembling. If they are old enough, they will be able to tell you about the dream — and you may become suspicious if the same bad dream is calmly described night after night as your child climbs into your bed!

It is extremely rare for a child to wake every night with nightmares. If you think this is happening, you should seek expert advice immediately.

Myth: 'My child is afraid of the dark'

Fear of the dark is also uncommon in young children. If they are used to being put down to sleep with the light off, they learn that there is nothing to fear from the darkness. If they have parents who are not concerned about the dark, they will probably accept it naturally as part of the daily routine. However, some parents are concerned about leaving a child in the dark and prefer to use a night light. If you want your child to have a light at night-time, make sure that it is a fairly dim light as brightness can be stimulating — and may show up lots of interesting distractions that will help to keep your child awake.

Myth: 'My child is hyperactive'

A tendency to be over-active is not uncommon in young children and can occur for a number of reasons. The most common reason is lack of sleep. One of the most noticeable changes in these children when they learn to get the sleep they need is that their activity level reduces to normal, and they become less irritable and more able to concentrate.

Other reasons for over-activity include sensitivities or allergies to certain foods and hyperactivity related to abnormal brain functioning. Both of these are rare and may be alleviated with medical attention. Where diet is a problem, observant parents can make adjustments by experimenting with different foods.

But remember that the most common cause of over-activity is lack of sleep. It is not helpful for anyone to label your child hyperactive if what they most need is to learn new sleep habits.

Myth: 'Medication helps'

Most parents who have tried using medication to get their child to sleep know about this myth. It is a very common solution, tried — often reluctantly — by many parents of children who have sleep problems. Results vary with different drugs and different children. Some parents report that their children are tired and irritable during the day when they have been given medication the night before. Others find that there is little improvement or that success is only temporary. And when they stop giving medication, parents generally find that their child's sleep pattern is as bad as ever because nothing new has been learned that will help the child sleep through the night.

Some parents decide to give their children medication occasionally when they are desperate for sleep themselves. Doing this may help parents to catch up on much-needed sleep but it is most unlikely to have any long-term effects on their child's sleep habits.

Myth: 'I'll cut out the daytime sleep so they'll be ready to sleep at night'

In fact, the opposite seems to happen. Children who are tired from the lack of a daytime sleep can take longer to settle at night and may also sleep for a shorter time. Similarly, when children sleep well at night, they are often much happier about having a daytime sleep.

When children do fall asleep from sheer exhaustion, they have learned nothing about going to sleep at other times when they are not so tired.

Myth: 'My child is only difficult because of daylight saving'
Children are experts at picking up signals from their parents. If
you expect your child to go to bed regardless of whether it's light
or dark outside — and providing you are both quite clear about
this — they are likely to settle without any fuss. But if you don't
feel confident that they will go to bed and you look for excuses
for their behaviour, then your child is likely to pick up your doubts
and make the most of them.

   If you don't feel confident about them sleeping during daylight
hours, it may help to try to darken the room as much as possible.
You could do this by pulling the curtains or perhaps by pinning
a dark towel over the window as a temporary arrangement during
the summer months. Your child is not going to worry if this practical
arrangement looks a bit strange — it will be dark and they will
be asleep.

**Myth: 'My child is a Leo' or 'They're just like my wife/
husband's side of the family and don't need much sleep'**
There are some things about your child's personality and background
over which you have little control — but sleep is not one of them.
Some children learn to sleep through the night much easier than
others, but sleep patterns are not fixed forever. New patterns can
be learned by children — and can be taught by parents.

Myth: 'We've tried everything'
Many parents have tried everything they can think of to get their
child sleeping through the night, and they feel really defeated when
nothing seems to work. This book offers a method that has been
tried successfully by hundreds of families. It is a method we offer
confidently, knowing that it has worked for almost all the families
who have used it as we suggest.

Myth: 'My child will cry all night if left alone'
Not true — though it may seem like it at times.

**And the most paralysing myth of all: 'It's my fault' or
'I've done everything wrong' or 'I'm a hopeless parent'**
There's nothing like a child with sleep problems to shake your
confidence as a parent. But it's a problem that can happen to any
parents, despite their best intentions and despite all their efforts
to deal with it. Give yourself some credit — it's not easy when
you're struggling to deal with a tired, grizzly child during the day
and at night. And if you feel exhausted yourself most of the time,

you really deserve a medal just for surviving — not all the criticism you heap on yourself.

The truth is that night-waking is not anyone's fault. Neither you nor your child is to blame. Research over the past decade has shown that sleep problems arise from a complex interaction of factors such as the temperament a child is born with, and how the parents and child respond to each other. Often some of the contributing factors are outside the parents' control — things that just happen that way.

In the next chapter we look at some of the more common ways that sleep problems begin.

How did it start?

Many parents look for clues to solving their child's sleep problem by thinking about how it started, and different families come up with very different reasons. Some children seem to have never been good sleepers, right from birth. For some of them this has been caused by a medical problem that interrupted sleep early in their lives and got them off to a bad start. For others there's no obvious reason. They just seem to have been born that way.

Some families have one child who learns to sleep through quickly and easily, followed by another who needs extra guidance. Clearly, there are differences between children right from birth, and having one who is a good sleeper is no guarantee when it comes to the second.

Some children start with a good sleep pattern but develop problems later. When this happens, parents can often date the problems from the time of some change in the child's routine. This could be anything from an illness to moving house. It might have happened at the time of changing from cot to bed or when the family went on holiday. Or once again, it might have happened for no obvious reason at all.

For a few children, sleep problems start as a reaction to something traumatic in their lives or in the lives of their parents. This might be something like a marriage separation or a death in the family. At such times children may need extra comfort at bedtime or when they wake during the night. After the crisis passes and the family gets back into a routine, some children will return to their previous good sleep patterns — but for others sleep problems will have become a habit.

Whatever the reason for your child's sleep problem, it's in the past and can't be changed. What you can change, however, is what's happening now. So while it may be interesting to know how your child's sleep problem started, it's much more useful to know what keeps it going.

What keeps it going?

When we first looked at families where a child had a sleep problem, we found a few common patterns emerging. Some of these may provide clues to help you work out what keeps your child's sleep problem going.

One common pattern was that there was often no regular night-time routine. Things happened in a different order every night, or maybe at different times. Consequently, children didn't always realise that bedtime was approaching, and they got a nasty shock when it was suddenly announced. So their natural reaction was to protest — and the nightly bedtime battle followed.

Another common pattern was that children and not their parents decided when it was bedtime. This caused problems because parents often thought it was bedtime before their children wanted to go — and a whole evening could pass while everyone waited for little Johnny or Suzie to finally crash.

Children falling asleep in the living area, or while feeding, or with a parent present, were all found to be frequent patterns in families with sleep problems. The trouble with this was when children stirred in the night — as we all tend to — they found themselves in a whole different situation from where they were when they went to sleep. Their last memory before they drifted off was of being in Mum or Dad's arms, or of sucking on a bottle, or of curling up on a lounge chair. Now they were somewhere different, with no bottle and no parent. So instead of quietly rolling over and going back to sleep, they woke themselves up properly with a full-blown roar. (Imagine how you would feel if you fell asleep in the chair where you are now sitting and woke later to find yourself mysteriously transported somewhere else.)

Another problem with this method was that children were not learning to go to sleep by themselves if parents sat with them until they settled, if they were rocked to sleep, or if they drifted off to sleep while feeding. Before they can learn to go to sleep by themselves, they have to have the opportunity.

24

Finally, in just about all cases where children were waking in the night, they were getting something out of it. Maybe they would call out or cry and someone would go in to talk with them, to cuddle them and to stay with them until they settled. Maybe they would get an extra feed or drink they didn't really need. They might get into Mum and Dad's bed and be allowed to stay there for the rest of the night. Or maybe on a bad night they would just get yelled at and told to 'stay in bed or else'. Even that is a form of attention, and if they sometimes get a better reception, it's worth the risk. The conclusion to draw from all this is that when children are being rewarded in some way for waking in the night, they are unlikely to want to give it up.

These common patterns provide some ideas about what keeps a sleep problem going. Some of them might have been happening in your home. Despite all your best intentions to the contrary, you might have inadvertently helped to keep the problem going. If you have, you can be sure you are not alone. You are in the good company of many other parents who love their children and who have done whatever they thought was best in the circumstances.

With the benefits of hindsight, you may now be wishing that you had handled some things differently. This is inevitable when you consider that you are learning your job as you go. No-one teaches you how to be a parent.

There is no time to blame yourself or anyone else for your child's sleep problem. Instead, you could choose to use your time and energy for making changes. So let's get on with it!

Let's get on with it

The Leslie (Centre) method of getting babies to sleep works beautifully! Peace and sleep for baby! Peace and sleep for distraught parents!
(G.R.N., Otago — *N.Z. Woman's Weekly*)

Step one: Tell your child what you expect

Be absolutely clear in your own mind about what you are going to do so you will convey confidence and authority when you explain the situation. Tell your child clearly that there are going to be some new rules in your household, and describe what is going to happen. And tell them enthusiastically how pleased you are going to be in the morning, after they have stayed quietly in bed all night. Make this sound like something special they can do because they are so grown up, and not like a punishment.

You might be surprised to find how quickly a child can pick up the signals from a parent who is clear about what they expect, and confident and determined that they will get it. Children who get this message are much more likely to accept the new rules because they know that you really mean what you say. And this goes for babies too young to understand much of what you are saying. They can pick up your determination from the way you speak, from the way you handle them, and from your whole manner. Babies of nine months and even younger have been known to start sleeping through the night immediately they sense this new confidence and determination in their parents, without any other changes having to be made.

Step two: The bedtime routine

Routines may be boring but they work. They let your child know that events are leading up to bedtime so they know what to expect. Remember, they can't tell the time, so without a routine the sudden announcement that it is bedtime can be a nasty surprise.

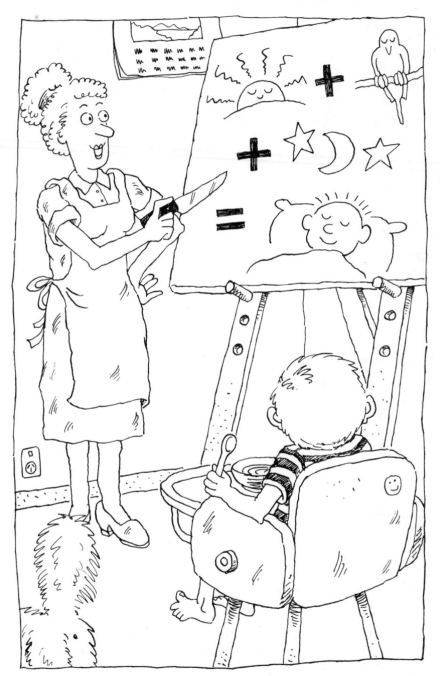

Tell your child clearly that there are going to be some new rules in your household, and describe what is going to happen.

Choose a routine to suit your household. It might be dinner, followed by bath, quiet game or story, clean teeth, toilet and then bed. There'll be time for cuddles with Mum or Dad in your routine, and for younger children there might be a final feed before bed. The routine will take care of all your child's last-minute needs for the day so you can put them to bed feeling confident that what is most needed now is a good sleep.

A word of warning: Make sure that last half-hour before bedtime isn't too hectic. Children need to wind down before going to bed or they may get over-excited and find it hard to settle. This is particularly important for parents to remember if they happen to arrive home at bedtime and want some time with their children. Make it a quiet time and save those energetic games for when you don't want them to be sleepy. Remember that it's the quality of the time you have with your child that is important, not the noisiness or level of activity.

Some children recognise that their routine is leading up to bedtime and decide not to co-operate at an earlier stage — perhaps by refusing to have a bath or to put on pyjamas. If this happens, proceed with the routine calmly and firmly and try not to be distracted by the protests.

Bedtime is the time you set and not when your child chooses
Be clear in your own mind what time you want them to go to bed and stick to it. This gives you control of your evenings and control of your child's sleeping habits. They will feel secure knowing that the rules are clear and that you are in charge. And both you and your child will benefit when you have some time for yourself, some time for your friends and time for your partner. So decide now what time you want your child to go to bed and work towards this.

Bedrooms are for sleeping in
They are not for playing games, feeding, drinking, and reading stories. To help your child learn that they are expected to go to sleep in their bedroom, it's best if you cut out all the other activities they might expect to enjoy there. Until a good sleep pattern has been established, make sure that these other activities happen somewhere else. This way the rules are very clear and there's less room for misunderstanding at bedtime.

If your child likes a story before bed, read it in the living-room just before bedtime. If they need a drink, give it as part of the bedtime routine — but not in the bedroom, and perhaps twenty

Bedtime is the time you set and not when your child chooses.

minutes before bed. If they like a game before bed, that too can happen in the living area — otherwise it can become a marvellous delaying tactic as the child pleads for 'just one more' before you can escape from the bedroom. And if they are in the bedroom with Teddy, busily engrossed in a visit to the farm animals, they are not likely to want to stop just because you think it's time to go to sleep. Make it easier for your child to distinguish between play-time and sleep-time by keeping play out of the bedroom at this time of night.

Of course, this doesn't mean that your child can't take a favourite cuddly toy or special blanket to bed. But make sure it's something large enough to be easily located in the middle of the night. One of the main problems with smaller items such as dummies is that they tend to get lost among the blankets and cause disrupted sleep for the whole household in the panic to find them. If your child is used to going to sleep with a dummy, they're likely to want it to get back to sleep when they stir in the night — and you're likely to be woken to help find it. More about dummies later.

Learning to sleep through the night
starts with learning to go to sleep alone

Lots of parents rock their children to sleep, sit with them until they settle, or let them fall asleep while feeding or watching T.V. This may take time but it usually works eventually and may avoid an awful scene over bedtime. However, we have already seen how this way teaches children nothing about going to sleep by themselves — and they are more likely to keep waking in the night.

If you want your child to learn to go to sleep alone, you have to give them the opportunity. It's not something that can be learned with you present. If you want them to feel secure when they stir in the night — because everything is just as it was at bedtime — then they must fall asleep alone. This way they are much more likely to roll over and go back to sleep quietly when they stir rather than scream a protest that they've been deserted. And because your child had gone to sleep alone when they first settled, they'll know how to do it again during the night — without your help to settle down again.

Similarly, children should go to bed awake. It's very tempting to pop them into bed without disturbing them if they have dozed off to sleep in the armchair. But you're asking for trouble when they wake up and find themselves somewhere else later in the night. They need to learn that bed is a good place for going to sleep, and they need to be saved from any nasty shocks in the middle of the night. So if your child falls asleep before getting to bed, don't carry them there so gently that they don't know what's happening. Pick them up in a matter-of-fact way so they're sufficiently awake to know where they are. Then tuck them into bed, give them a goodnight kiss, tell them you'll see them in the morning ... and leave.

Step three: Teaching your child to settle alone

Your child is not likely to give in easily just because you've said goodnight and walked out of the bedroom! They're used to having you with them. They're used to getting out of bed. They're used to trying every trick to get you back in there. Perhaps they want another drink or want to go to the toilet — again! Or maybe 'Teddy's lonely.' If this sort of thing is happening every night, and if you've done everything you can to meet all your child's needs before bed, you'll be able to recognise delaying tactics when you hear them. Here's how to deal with some of the more common ways that might be tried to get your attention and so trick you into rewarding your child for staying awake.

Calling out
Don't respond. You know your child doesn't really need anything and you know they're just trying to get your attention in order to delay the final goodnight. They want to be with you because they enjoy your company and have got into the habit of getting your attention to prolong bedtime. But they don't *need* to be with you — they need a good night's sleep. By not attending to them you will be giving them a very powerful message that calling out at bedtime doesn't work — and your child will learn to go to sleep instead.

A word of warning
Of course you go in if you think there's something really wrong. Try to check from the door, without speaking, in case you're being conned.
It is also essential that you make the bedroom as safe as possible before you leave the child in there alone. Make sure there's nothing that is dangerous or that can be damaged.
This is important for the child's safety and for your confidence about leaving them. If you have any doubts at all that something has gone wrong, *go in and check.*

It's even more powerful to leave them than to respond with yelling, smacking and threats to 'Go to sleep or you'll get a smack!' All these are a form of attention that can make it worthwhile to keep calling out.

Crying is the most powerful way to get you into the room
Your newborn baby cried when they needed something, and all your instincts told you to attend to them. But now they're older, and crying doesn't always mean that they need something. Sometimes it just means that they haven't got their own way. Chances are you can tell the difference between a real distress cry and a tantrum cry — and most likely the cry you are hearing at bedtime is telling you what the child wants rather than what they need.

If crying works to get your attention, you are teaching your child to cry. They're not going to give it up if it's the only thing that gets you into the room. So if you want your child to stop crying at bedtime and go to sleep alone, you have to teach them that crying doesn't work and you have to ignore it.

Once again, if you have any doubts at all that something might be wrong, *check*. We are certainly not advising you to ignore a child who is ill, who is hurt, or who genuinely needs something. Before you leave a child to cry, you should feel confident that they are safe, healthy, and that all their needs for warmth, food and toiletting have been met as far as possible.

It's not easy to leave a child to cry. Screaming, raging or, worse still, heart-rending sobs can shake all your convictions that you are doing the right thing. So go easy on yourself. Remind yourself that you are doing this in your child's interests to teach them a new skill that will be good for them and good for your family. Close the doors between yourself and the noise, turn up the T.V., make yourself a cup of coffee — or go for a walk and let your more determined partner cope. Above all, make sure you have some support if you are alone. Invite a friend in for company or have someone on standby who agrees with what you are doing and whom you can phone. If you have a partner, make sure you both agree that you're going to leave your child to cry, and help each other through the hard part. It's stressful enough listening to the crying without having an argument at the same time about whether or not you should be doing it.

It might also help you to leave your child to cry at bedtime if you bear in mind our confidence that it works, and that it's not going to do the child any harm. Just how quickly it works varies from child to child. Some will get the message on the first night, and others will still be trying a week later. But nearly all parents can see an improvement after two or three nights. They quickly find that their child is not crying so long, or so hard, after being left for a few nights. And of the hundreds of families we have worked with, none has ever reported that they felt it had done their child any harm. On the contrary, lots of people noticed an improvement in their child and in their relationship with their child — as we saw in chapter two. More about that later.

Getting out of bed is another common delaying tactic at bedtime

Once again, you have to teach your child that it doesn't work — that it won't get you hooked into a conversation, it won't get them a few more minutes of your time, or another biscuit, or any of the other good things that make getting up worthwhile. Don't speak to them and try not to even look at them. Just lead them straight back to bed with a minimum of attention. Picture yourself as a robot and you'll get the general idea. You're not pleased to see the child, you are calm and firm, you don't speak, smile or growl!

If they keep coming out, close the door — and if necessary hold it closed, or find another way that it can't be opened. This can be done by putting a latch on the door, putting a wedge under the door or perhaps tying the door handle to another door further down the hall. If you are determined to keep the child in the bedroom, you will find a way that suits you and your home.

If they like to have their door open, tell them that it will be left open as long as they stay in bed. This way they learn that they have a choice — to stay in bed with the door open, or to get up and have it closed. If you have to close the door, tell your child that the door will be opened again once they have settled quietly in bed. Check after they've been settled for ten minutes and then leave the door open.

Eventually the child will fall asleep. Whether it takes five minutes or two hours, whether it seems incredibly difficult or much easier than you expected — stop and give yourself some credit at this stage. You have crossed the first major hurdle in teaching your child to sleep through the night, and they have had their first experience of going to sleep alone. Now you both know that it can be done. Next time may be easier for all of you.

Getting out of bed is another common delaying tactic at bedtime.

The next thing you need to be prepared for is waking in the night

We have already seen how children keep waking in the night because they get something out of it, usually when they get into your room, or when they get you to come to them. So the best way to stop night-waking is to stop making it worthwhile. You do this in the same way as you teach your child to settle at the beginning of the night. You don't respond to crying or calling out. You return them to bed robot-like if they get up. (You'll probably find it very easy to act like a robot or a speechless zombie at 2 o'clock in the morning!) You close the door if they keep getting up.

Above all, don't let your child persuade you — when you know they don't really need attention — to feed or cuddle them, or let them into your bed. Any of these might help to settle them at the time, but they make it much more likely that they will wake up and expect the same treatment again the next night. Even if you give in only occasionally, your child will know that sometimes crying or getting out of bed works to get something they want — so it's worth a try. If you want them to stop waking from habit, you will have to teach them that you only attend during the night when they really need something.

Some children are really cunning about sneaking into their parents' bed without being noticed. If you sometimes wake to find an extra little body in the bed, you have accidentally rewarded your child's night-waking without even knowing it was happening. If you want this to stop, you have to make sure you know when it happens so you can return the child immediately to bed. Make sure they wake you when they come into your room by having to make some sort of noise to get there. For example, if your bedroom door doesn't creak loudly enough when pushed wide open, you could help it along by hanging bells from the door handle or by using a can of pebbles for a door-stop.

Getting-up time is when you decide, not when your child chooses or when the sun happens to rise

In most homes, 4.00 a.m. is a little too early, even in summer! Be really clear about how long you want your child to stay in bed and what time you would be happy for them to get up. Treat waking before this time just as you treat any waking in the night. Don't respond to calling out, and if your child gets up, take them back to bed.

The best way to stop night-waking is to stop making it worthwhile.

Since your child can't read the time, it's helpful if you can give a clear sign when it's time to get up. This could be a sound such as an alarm or a radio, or it could be the time that you call out or go to your child's room to greet them.

Many families like to get the day off to a happy start by having a few minutes when the children pile into their parents' bed. In these families younger children can learn that it's time to get up when their parents come to the cot to collect them — although older children will probably not wait for an invitation. Children can learn that you are pleased to see them if they arrive by your bedside after a good night's sleep but that they will be taken back to bed if they wake too early.

Other parents like to get up before their child's waking time in order to get a few early-morning chores completed. Older children can learn that a parent's getting-up time is not necessarily a signal that their day has started, and even from a young age, children who wake early can learn to play happily in bed for a while if they have a few soft toys or books at hand. But to be realistic, once your child has had a good night's sleep, they're likely to be keen to see you — and it's good for them to know that you are pleased to see them too. You can't expect them to remain confined to bed if they have woken at a reasonable time.

If your child wakes crying for attention and is still doing so when it's time to get up, you will eventually have to attend to them. But it is important for them to know that you have arrived because it's time to get up and not because they have been crying. You could demonstrate this by going in during a lull — even when they're catching their breath — so your presence doesn't seem to be a response to the crying. You could even underline the point by saying, 'It's getting-up time now', and not making the big fuss you would make when you were really pleased with them for staying quietly in bed.

In the morning, give lots of praise
and encouragement for success

When your child sleeps through the whole night you *are* really pleased — so show it. Tell them how pleased you are. You might like to give a special reward — time in your bed before you get up, a favourite breakfast, or a phone call to grandparents to tell them the good news. All the family should join in the praise so your child learns that they get lots of attention for sleeping through — and so they're much more likely to want to do it again.

All the family should join in the praise.

Attend to improvements

A child is not likely to sleep through the first night you try this plan, but very soon you will notice some improvements. Perhaps they cry for only ten minutes instead of thirty before settling. Perhaps they wake twice in the night, when they woke six times the night before. Or perhaps they stay in bed until you call in the morning. Notice what they get right, and notice the improvements. They're having to learn many new things so they need lots of encouragement. Praise them enthusiastically for every improvement so they will want to do even better the next night.

If there's no immediate improvement — stay calm!

Children have to know that you mean what you say, and the best way to find out is to test the rules. If your child has always made the decision about bedtime in the past, they're not likely to give up after one night. And if they sometimes got something good when they woke in the night, they're going to have to try a few times before they really believe that it is not going to happen again.

If you have survived a really bad night when your child has cried for a long time or woken a lot during the night, this is no time to give up. Give yourself lots of praise and lots of credit. By resisting the temptation to go in to your child, you've done something that can be very difficult for you but is in the best interests of your child. They have already started to learn that you no longer attend to night-waking, and you are not likely to have more than two or three bad nights before you see an improvement. Until the improvement happens, just show your child calmly in the morning that you are not pleased. Do this in a matter-of-fact way, without being angry and without trying to punish them. Remember that they have stayed alone all night, perhaps for the first time ever. Put the emphasis on the improvement you expect: 'Perhaps you will sleep better tonight.' Don't make a big fuss first thing in the morning. Don't give any rewards you might have planned, but explain why they're not getting them. Then continue the day as usual. As bedtime approaches you could remind them of the new rules and speak enthusiastically once again about how pleased you will be when they sleep through the night.

Daytime sleep (or rest time) can be managed almost the same as night-time

You decide when and how much sleep your child should have. As far as possible, you make sleep or rest a regular part of the daily routine. You put them to bed and leave them there. If necessary, you keep the door closed and — for older children — see that the window is escape-proof!

The main difference with daytime sleep is that your child will not always go to sleep before it's time to get up again. This might be because they have not yet learned a routine of having a daytime sleep when you want them to or — particularly with an older child — it might be that a quiet rest without sleep is all that is needed.

You can insist that your child go to bed at a regular time during the day just as you do at night. This gives you a break and it gives them an opportunity for a sleep or rest — whichever is needed. You can decide how long the rest should be. One hour is probably as long as you can expect them to be quiet if they are resting, and it's probably the most you can stand if they continue protesting loudly about being in their room.

If your child has not settled after an hour, they're probably not going to — or else they're going to sleep too late and be wide awake next time you want them to go to bed. If you have to get them up while they're still crying, once again try to catch them when they're taking a breath. This shows that you are getting them up because it's time and doesn't encourage them to think that crying gets them up when they want. Be a bit matter-of-fact to show that you are not pleased, but remember to praise them if they have been asleep or quiet for part of the time.

If your child goes to sleep, let them sleep for as long as you like. But keep in mind that they're not likely to be sleepy at bedtime if they sleep much later than 3.00 p.m. If they just have a rest, let them know when rest time is over, and praise them for being quiet and for resting. Remember, rests are good for both of you.

Keep a record so you can check on your progress

Make a note of what time your child goes to bed, how long it takes them to settle, how many times they wake through the night and how long they are awake during the night. Note also the time they wake in the morning. Start the record three or four nights before you start teaching your child to sleep through the night, and continue for the first week of the new regime. Then three weeks later, record again for a week to see how you are doing.

Finally, the results

Most parents notice a change in their child's sleep pattern within three nights and a major improvement within a week. After using this plan for a month, almost all parents find that their child is settling well and sleeping through most nights.

If you have achieved this goal — congratulations! You decided what you wanted and you persevered until you got there. Already you and your child will be reaping the benefits.

If it hasn't worked so well after a month, there's probably a good reason. Perhaps your child got sick at some stage and you had to interrupt the plan to attend to them during the night. That's discouraging, but it doesn't mean you have to give up. Just start again as soon as they're well enough. Or perhaps your resolve faltered on a bad night, or they managed to persuade you to attend to them sometimes when they didn't really need you. This is understandable, but it means that the rules are not so clear for your child and it's harder for them to learn. It still doesn't mean that you should give up. It just means that you need to be a bit more determined and that it's going to take a bit longer. If you are not satisfied with the improvements after about ten days, you may decide to seek further help. Some suggestions about how to do this can be found at the end of the book.

Yes, but . . .

So, you've read through the plan but you've still got some doubts about it. Or maybe there's some reason why you think it might work for other people but not for you. In this chapter we try to deal with some of the concerns most often expressed by parents before they decide to put the plan into action.

Won't my child feel unloved and insecure if I ignore them?
In our experience the children who feel most secure are those who have clear rules and know their parents are in charge. It's pretty scary to be only two years old and find yourself the most powerful person in the household! When parents take control they feel more confident and less resentful. When children and parents get a good night's sleep they have more energy to enjoy each other the next day. Parents feel more tolerant, and children's behaviour improves.

Children who have learned to sleep through the night often seem to feel *more* loved and *more* secure. Of the hundreds of families we have seen, many have reported that their children are happier and that they enjoy a better relationship with their children after using this plan. None have reported that they think it did any harm.

Obviously, we are not recommending that you ignore your child or leave them to cry as a general rule. During the day you give them lots of love and attention. When you are called to admire the latest creation with crayons or blocks, you respond. When they fall over and hurt themselves, or jam a finger in the door and cry, you comfort them. Whenever they really need you — day or night — you attend to them. We're suggesting that you distinguish between what they want and what they need. We're also suggesting that your presence at night is being demanded from habit — and because your child enjoys being with you. You will encourage this habit if you continue to attend to these demands.

But I don't want to break my child's spirit
It's important to remember that you are teaching your child a new skill, that you are trying to change a habit and not a personality.

42

You are not 'going into battle' and you will not 'break their spirit' or 'suppress their individuality'. You are simply using your adult wisdom to make a decision about what is best for your child — just as you do in many other areas of their life.

How long should I leave my child to cry?
Until they stop! If you find you can't stand it any longer, and you give in after ten minutes, or an hour, or two hours, then you are just teaching them to cry longer. You are teaching them that crying works if they just keep it up for long enough. You have to teach them that crying doesn't work to get your attention, no matter how long it is kept up. You will make it much easier for them to learn this if you are firm and consistent about it right from the beginning.

But they will cry for hours
They may cry for quite a while the first few nights. It might be thirty minutes, an hour or two, or even longer if they are really determined. But they won't cry at the same intensity throughout this time. Sometimes the cry will drop to a grizzle, or even a pause while they listen to see if there's any response. And it won't go on forever. Most likely you will notice an improvement after the first two or three nights. The length of time they cry will soon drop and they may well be sleeping through some nights before the end of the week. Lots of children learn to settle happily and sleep through the night during the second week, and even the most reluctant are usually sleeping well within a month. But you should be prepared for a few bad nights before they learn the new rules, and you should expect the odd bout of crying some nights during the first few weeks. Your child is not likely to be pleased to find that they no longer get their own way, and they're likely to test the new rules — and you — as part of learning to sleep through the night.

Can't I attend to them at all?
Of course you attend if you think there may be something really wrong — if the angry cry turns into one of pain, or if you are worried about safety. Try to check from the door, and attend to the problem in a matter-of-fact way — such as untangling them from the sheet without lots of extra attention. If nothing seems wrong and you decide you've been conned, get out fast and continue as you were.

But what if they're sick?
When a child is sick they might need medication, extra drinks, or just your comfort and reassurance during the night. Of course you attend to them at these times. Once they're well again you can resume the plan.

But what about teething?
The best way for children to make teething time go quickly is to sleep through it — and many do just this. Teething is, after all, a natural process, and often teeth just appear one day. A few children do, however, have teething difficulties and are miserable for a few hours or even a few days before a tooth comes through. Night-times can be worse because there are fewer distractions. But if teething does not bother your child much during the day, don't expect it to be much worse at night. At worst, we calculate that it takes an average of three days each for your child's set of twenty teeth to come through, so during the first two years you might expect to have sixty difficult days. That leaves a total of 670 nights with no teething!

There's not much you can do about teething. If you think teething gel or pain relief is necessary during the night, attend to this in the usual way and then leave.

But my child falls asleep before going to bed
It's very tempting to leave a child like that, but until they learn to sleep through the night they should go to bed awake. So wake them up just enough to let them know they're going to bed. They don't have to be wide awake, just as long as you can get a drowsy response and you know they're aware of what's happening.

But they will try to climb out of the cot
If they can get out of the cot, but not back into it, it will be hard for them to settle without getting you into the room to help. And if that's the only thing that gets you in there, they're pretty sure to do it! Also, there's a danger that they may be hurt if they try to climb out of the cot. This could be the time to move them to a bed, or at least to a mattress on the floor for a while. You know how to handle it if they then get out of bed.

But my child throws the blankets off and might get cold
So put an extra layer of clothes on to make sure they keep warm if they get uncovered. When they've settled down to sleep you can

sneak in to put the blankets back in place. As the child gets older, you can teach them to pull up their own blankets.

But my child gets really upset when I leave
They may scream, sob, whimper, shout, threaten or plead. They may tell you they love you, tell you they hate you, bang the door, bang their head or have a tantrum. They may try anything they think will work to get what they want. They don't like the new rules and are likely to test you to find out what it takes to make you give in. When they find that none of these tactics work they should abandon them after a few nights — and start to learn new ways of going to bed happily.

But they will fall asleep on the floor
Occasionally some children fall asleep in an exhausted heap on the floor after they have tried every trick they know to get out of the bedroom. If this happens with your child, wait until they're asleep and then go and put some blankets on, or lift them quietly back into bed. Make sure they can get back into the bed when they want to by putting some cushions in place as a step if the bed is too high. As long as they can get back into bed, they are not likely to fall asleep on the floor more than two or three times. After a couple of nights on the floor most children decide that bed is a more comfortable alternative.

But we've tried leaving our child to cry and it doesn't work
There is usually a good reason for this. Perhaps your child was too young when left, or perhaps they were suffering from a medical problem, such as an ear infection, which you didn't know about. Perhaps you got discouraged and decided to try something else before your child had learned that crying wasn't going to get your attention; or perhaps you weren't confident about leaving them and attended at some times but not at others. You may have felt that you could only leave them for a certain time so they learned that you would finally attend if they cried a bit longer. Or perhaps you used some parts of the plan but missed out one of the other important steps.

Check through the plan again and think about how you could do it differently if you decided to try again.

But they might make a mess if I don't attend
Yes, they might dirty their pants, or perhaps just wet them. A few children even make themselves sick, especially if they've just had a large drink before bedtime. Generally this doesn't happen more

than once or twice. Just clean up the mess in a matter-of-fact way and leave the room. If they need changing, do it with a minimum of fuss — no smiles, cuddles or conversation, just a quick, businesslike change. And if they're still in nappies, and they've only wet them, it's not going to do any harm if you leave them until morning. See that they keep warm, and cover their bottom with lots of vaseline to prevent irritation.

But they need someone or something for comfort at bedtime
Make sure they have a favourite cuddly toy or blanket to take to bed. Remember, Teddy needs as much sleep as the child does and can set a wonderful example.

**My child's dummy gets lost and
they won't go back to sleep without it**
Then you're in trouble! Some people find safe ways of attaching the dummy to their child or to the cot, but using string or safety pins to do this can be dangerous. Even if you can find a safe way to keep the dummy close at hand, the child may still not be able to locate it in the dark. You have to decide whether you want to get up immediately every time they cry and retrieve the dummy or whether you want to discard the dummy altogether so they can learn to go to sleep alone. It usually takes only a few nights before children learn to settle without a dummy — and before the whole household can enjoy uninterrupted sleep.

But I am still breast-feeding
You can still teach your child to sleep through the night. Just make sure the last feed is twenty minutes or so before bedtime. If they drift off to sleep on the breast, see that they wake up enough to know what's happening when put to bed.

At first you may find that your milk comes in when you hear your child crying in the night. This is a natural response and nothing to be concerned about. If you need to, express the milk so you feel more comfortable.

But my child's still hungry in the middle of the night
If your child is over nine months and is still having a big feed during the night, it might be that they're not getting enough to eat during the day. A vicious circle can develop when your child is not hungry and doesn't eat or drink much during the day because they are having such a good feed at night. Most parents with this problem find that the routine can be changed surprisingly quickly

when they decide to phase out night feeding. They soon have a child who is not only sleeping better at night but feeding better during the day as well.

But they need to go to the toilet in the night
Teaching your child to sleep through the night, at the same time that they are learning to be dry, can be a bit tricky. You may have to decide which of these skills you want learned first so you can concentrate on teaching one at a time. Otherwise you may find that they 'want potty' several times every night because it's the one thing that works to get your attention after bedtime.

If your child is able to go to the toilet alone during the day but is unwilling to do so at night, you may choose to assist this in a quick, businesslike manner. You can also be encouraging in other ways — perhaps making it easier by leaving a potty near the bed or a light on in the hall. As soon as your child is ready, you can teach all the skills they need to go alone and encourage them to be more grown-up.

But my child is afraid of the dark
Very few children are really afraid of the dark. It doesn't usually occur to them until someone suggests it. If you have tried to understand your child's night-waking by asking, 'Don't you like the dark?', you might just have planted an idea for them to use. You can help overcome this by talking about how good darkness is for getting to sleep and how you like to go to sleep in the dark. If you think that there is genuine fear of the dark and you want to use a night-light, make sure it's fairly dim. As we mentioned earlier, light can help keep children awake. Some parents compromise by leaving a hall light on with the bedroom door slightly ajar. If your child likes to have a light, they will quickly learn to stay in bed so the door remains open.

But my child has nightmares
Nightmares can begin to be troublesome for a few children from the age of three. At this age some children find it hard to separate fantasy from reality. You can help by keeping bedtime free from frightening stories or scary T.V. programmes. And talk to your child sometimes about how stories are 'just pretend' and not really true.

If your child is having the occasional nightmare, they might need you to comfort them in the night. If it's happening frequently, they might need professional help. But if the child shows no signs of distress while describing frequent nightmares, it may pay to be a bit suspicious. They might have learned that saying they've had a nightmare always works to get into your bed!

But if I put my child to sleep later at night, they should wake up later in the morning

It would be nice if you could put them to bed late on the night before those days when you want to sleep in, but unfortunately it's not that simple. Putting your child to bed late will just make them grumpy in the morning — it's unlikely to have much effect on the time they're used to waking up. If early waking is a problem, you can gradually teach them to sleep longer, or to play quietly until getting-up time. Decide on the earliest time you are prepared to attend to them — say 5.30 a.m. Once your child is quiet until that time, keep extending getting-up time by fifteen to twenty minutes until you reach the reasonable time you want.

But my children share a room

You might be able to remove the good sleeper for a few nights — perhaps arrange for them to have a sleeping bag in the living room as a special treat, or let them stay at a friend's place.

Even if you can't change the sleeping arrangements, you can involve any other children and adults in the household in the plan. Make sure they know not to attend and that they are part of the 'praise team' after a successful night. Praise and encourage the other members of the family for their help.

My child shares a room with me

You can usually get your child settled before you go to bed at night, and then treat night-waking just as you would if they were in a separate room — don't respond to crying and put them straight back to bed if they get up. It can be a bit more difficult to do this when they know you are present, and some parents get around this problem by choosing to sleep in the living room for a few nights until their child has started to sleep through.

But mine are twins

When twins are waking each other at night, it's sometimes wise to separate them temporarily until they have both learned to sleep through. But if you are unable to do this — or if they manage to wake each other despite your best efforts to prevent it — persevere. When one twin refuses to settle or wakes during the night, control your urge to rush in and attend to one before the other wakes. This would only encourage the first to continue waking — and to continue demanding your attention during the night. Leave the waker, just as you would leave one child who was learning to sleep through the night. And if they both wake — leave them both. It sometimes takes longer when you are teaching two children to sleep at the same time, but it still works.

Life will be easier when your twins have similar sleep patterns, so insist that bedtime is the same for both of them. If one wakes before the other at a reasonable time in the morning, teach them to stay quietly in bed until the other twin wakes — or wake the other one yourself. This way they will both have had roughly the same amount of sleep and will be ready for the next sleep at the same time. During the day, try to arrange for them to get some individual attention. This way they won't need to take advantage of having your undivided attention at 5.00 a.m. when the other twin happens to be sleeping soundly.

But my child has a medical problem

If your child has special medical needs, or a medical condition such as asthma, a heart problem or reflux problem, it is very important to check with your G.P. or specialist before using this plan. Any medical condition that causes you to have doubts about the wisdom of leaving your child to cry should be checked out with the experts. This is not only essential for the safety of your child but also essential to give you the confidence you need before using the plan.

Many parents of children with medical problems have been able to use the plan successfully once they have been reassured by their doctors that it is safe to do so.

But what about colic?

Most children will grow out of colic by the time they are three or four months old, but a few continue to suffer similar symptoms as a reaction to solid foods, or because of sensitivity to some kinds of food. Until you know which foods your child should avoid, it is more difficult to teach them to sleep at night because they may need your attention quite often. It will be easier once you have established a list of foods that will not be upsetting, providing you don't experiment with anything new in the diet until a regular sleep routine is established.

The trick here is to know when your child is suffering from pain and when they are just wanting your attention from habit. Whenever you think they are suffering from symptoms like colic, naturally you attend to them — just as you attend to any illness to offer whatever comfort and relief you can. However, if you walk into the

You need each other's support and you don't need to be arguing about it.

room to find a child who sits up happily and grins at you, the best thing to do is probably to turn smartly on your heels and leave. This way they learn that you are there when they need you but that you expect them to sleep through the night at other times.

But my partner disagrees with the plan

Then *don't start!* You need each other's support and you *don't* need to be arguing about it in the middle of the night. You won't teach your child to sleep if one of you is ignoring their cries and the other one is attending to them. Make sure you are agreed on your approach before you start. This is a family affair; it's something from which you'll all benefit and in which you all need to co-operate.

A suggestion: When all else fails to get your partner's agreement, let them be the one to get up in the night every time. This takes the pressure off you and might even help bring about a change of mind in your partner.

But I'm a single parent

It can be more difficult when you have to carry out this plan on your own, but lots of single parents have successfully done so. You may find it helpful to get some support from a sympathetic friend or from a member of your family. Find someone who agrees with your plan and ask them to come and stay with you, or to be available at the end of the phone. Warn them that you might need them in the middle of the night, when you feel tempted to give up.

Choose the time to put your plan into action carefully so you don't have too much strain during the day at the same time. If necessary, call in a babysitter during the day while you catch up on lost sleep.

What about the neighbours?

If you have close neighbours, it might help to explain what you are doing. They probably know already about the problems you've been having and they are likely to support your plan for change. Most neighbours are prepared to endure a loud night or two if they know it's in a good cause.

But will it work for me?

Yes, if you want it to. The success rate of this method is almost 100 per cent for those parents who use it as we suggest. If you only partially use the plan, or are inconsistent in using it, it may still work, but it will take longer and it will be more difficult.

Are you ready to start?

Here's a checklist:

- Do you know what you are going to do?
- Do all adults in the household agree about this?
- Have you got your support system planned?
- Have you checked out any medical problems with your doctor?
- Have you decided on the best sleeping arrangements for your child? Bed or cot? Light on or off? Sharing a room or alone?
- What is your routine before bedtime? Perhaps write it down.
- What time is bedtime?
- Do you know what you are going to do if your child cries or calls out?
- Do you know what you are going to do if your child gets out of bed?
- Are you clear about the times when you *should* attend to your child?
- Do you know what you are going to do in the morning? If it's been a good night, what rewards? ... or if it's not been a good night?
- Have you told your child what is happening?
- Have you explained to the rest of the family and the neighbours what is happening? Do they know their part in helping?
- Do you know what records to keep?
- Most important: Do you feel determined to make it work?

If you can answer 'yes' to all these questions, then you're ready to start. We won't wish you good luck because we know it works. All you need is good management.

Making it last

Let's assume that you've followed all the advice given in the previous chapters and that your whole family is now enjoying glorious nights of uninterrupted sleep. You may be feeling relaxed and confident about this, or you may be plagued by nervous doubts: 'How long will it last?'

You can make it last by being consistent and by knowing how to deal with any disruptions that are likely to occur.

One thing you will be finding now your child is sleeping through the night is that it's much easier to tell when they really need you. When they cry or call out only occasionally, there's much more likely to be a real need than when they were calling out every night just from habit. But before you attend to that midnight call, there are some pitfalls you should be aware of.

Testing the system

It's very normal for children who have been taught to sleep well to test the system every now and again to see if the new rules still apply. Your child is probably doing just this if they creep into your room, cry or call out, but have nothing really wrong when you check. If this happens over a couple of nights, you can show that you still mean business by dealing with it just as you did when you first taught them to sleep. When they find that there is no worthwhile response from you, they should be sleeping through again within a night or two.

Illnesses

The best way to get through the night with a minor illness is to sleep through it, and the good sleeper can often do this. But sick children do sometimes need attention during the night, and this can disrupt the best routines. To make sure this is only a temporary setback, simply stop attending at night when your child recovers. You have taught them to sleep previously, and they should learn even faster the second time around.

Going away from home

Another disruption to your wonderful new sleep routine can occur with a change of setting. You might take your child on holiday — visiting friends or staying in a motel. You might leave them with grandparents for several days. For whatever reason, sooner or later you will want them to sleep somewhere different from their own familiar room.

Wherever possible, keep to the same routine that you have at home. Explain your routine to other people caring for your child and ask them to use it too. Many parents find that once their child has learned to sleep through the night, they will do so wherever they are. They may test once or twice to see if the rules are still the same as at home, but are likely to settle down happily once shown that they are.

Here's a word of encouragement from parents who went on holiday with their daughter, only a week after they had taught her to sleep through. They were tested the first night they were away: 'We left her to cry, and did likewise when she came into our bed the next morning at 5.00 a.m. For the remaining ten nights we were away she slept twelve hours a night.'

Occasionally it's not possible to stick to the usual routine when your child is away from home. If they decide to test the rules in a new situation, you may not feel able to leave them to cry, or you may not be able to persuade others to leave them. The child may discover that they're allowed to sleep in Grandma's bed when staying with her, or that Dad will make a fuss of them at 3.00 a.m. if it's all in the interests of not waking the family in the adjoining motel room. Take heart! Children can learn that there are different rules for different households, and you can tell them very clearly what the rules are at your place when they get back home.

Problems with daytime sleep

If you have night-time sleep under control but are still having no success with the daytime sleep, you might find that the whole situation deteriorates. When your child starts deciding whether or

Another disruption to your wonderful new sleep routine can occur with a change of setting.

not to have a daytime sleep or rest, they may well decide to take charge at night also. It is important for your child to know that you are strong enough to make these decisions, and that the rules are clear and consistent. So insist that they have a daytime sleep or rest for as long as it is needed — decide when you want them to go to bed and how long you want them to stay there — and persevere until the habit is established and they are going off happily as a matter of course.

Arrival of a new baby

The new baby is likely to mean broken sleep for parents for a while, but there is no reason why other children in the household should join in. Two o'clock in the morning is not the best time to keep reassuring older children that you love them as much as the new baby! In the morning you can praise them for being big enough to sleep all night in their own bed, and during the day you can give them all the love and attention they need.

Moving from cot to bed

The move from cot to bed can open up all sorts of exciting possibilities for the child who has been confined to a cot. Tell them how special they are now that they are old enough to have their own bed — and make it clear that you expect them to stay there all night.

If your angelic sleeper turns into a demon at this stage, have another look at the section 'Getting out of bed' (page 33).

Morning's getting earlier!

Some parents find that their child tries getting up earlier and earlier. Check that they know the right signal for getting-up time. It might be when the alarm rings, when you get up, or when you call. It's *not* when the sun rises, when the birds start chirping, or when your child happens to wake! Be clear about what time is O.K. for you, and return them to bed calmly and firmly if they get up before then. If you are happy for them to play quietly in bed, leave a toy or a book within easy reach. And keep up the praise for staying quietly in bed until it's a well-established habit.

Daylight saving

Often parents who have taught their children to go to bed at night and to get up when it's light lose their confidence about getting children to sleep when summer approaches and the daylight hours get longer. If you want your child to go to bed at their normal bedtime — despite the fact that the sun is still shining and the neighbours' kids are still playing outside the window — then you should stay with the usual routine. Children are much less likely to question it if you explain that it's bedtime, and if you are confident and determined that daylight saving is not going to alter this. On the other hand, if you give any hints that you don't really expect them to go to bed until it's dark, they're likely to make the most of your uncertainty and still be up two hours later.

You might find that heavy curtains, blinds or even a blanket or towel over the window help to darken the room so it's easier for your child to sleep — and easier for you to feel confident that they can do so.

Prevention is better than cure

If you've had one child who wouldn't sleep through the night, you're not going to want a repeat performance with the new baby. There are some things you can do to help prevent the problem arising.

As we mentioned earlier, you do not ignore a young baby who is crying. When your two-month-old cries at night, it is because they need something, so you get up to attend to them — usually by giving them a feed. But even from an early age you can start to teach the difference between night and day. Daytime feeds can be fun times, accompanied by lots of talking, cuddling and smiling. Night-time feeds can be more businesslike — for nutrition only. You will be amazed how early your baby will be aware of the difference.

Another way that you can help to prevent sleep problems arising is to put your baby to bed while they are still awake. That might sound contradictory, but think about it. If you rock them off to sleep, their last memory is of being safe in your arms. They don't get a chance to learn that the cot is also a nice place to go to sleep — and a nice place to wake up. So put them down awake or drowsy. That way they are more likely to wake gradually at the end of their sleep and to start babbling, rather than to wake screaming because they are in a different place. And it will be much easier for them to learn to go to sleep alone if that's what they're used to right from the beginning.

The regular routine before bedtime is also something you can start while your child's still young so they know when bedtime is approaching. And once you've met all their needs, it's fine to leave them for a few minutes to settle, although they may cry a little when first put down. A few tears at bedtime do not necessarily mean that there is anything wrong, and it won't help your child to settle if you are hovering about every thirty seconds. But don't leave them for too long. If they're still crying after ten minutes, you should check and try to find out what they want.

As they get older and you get to know them better, you will begin to recognise that your child has different cries for different occasions. There's the urgent 'I'm hungry now' cry, the tired 'I'm ready for sleep' cry, the 'Hey, where is everybody, I need company' cry — and the temper cry when they don't immediately get their own way. You will be learning to distinguish between what your child wants and what they need, and they will be learning that they are part of a family and that what they want can not always have top priority. This is an important part of growing up and gives you some vital clues about when you can leave them to cry and when you can expect them to sleep through the night.

The most important way that you avoid sleep problems is by conveying your confidence that you are in charge, and your clear expectations of when you want them to sleep. If you take it for granted that your child will sleep — regardless of the fact that it's broad daylight, there's a jack-hammer operating outside the window, and Aunty Joan and the kids have just arrived for a visit — then they're much less likely to have doubts about the matter.

On the other hand, if you creep about the house, terrified that the slightest squeak of a floorboard might disturb them, it probably will! If you want your child to be a good sleeper, put them down confident from the beginning that they can sleep through all the usual household noises. Don't feel obliged to tip-toe about, converse in hushed whispers, or to take the phone off the hook. Bear in mind that before birth your baby could hear lots of noises from the outside world, as well as all the sloshings and gurglings of Mum's body. The womb is, in fact, quite a noisy place, and the baby was used to sleeping there before they were born. So there's no reason why they should be unable to sleep through most household noises.

Where to go for help

In this book we have tried to give you all the information you need to teach your child to sleep through the night. We feel confident that most people who read this will be able to use the information without any further assistance.

The things we cannot offer in a book are the personal attention to your own particular situation, and the reassurance and moral support we provide for the families who come and see us. If you feel that you need more help than the book provides, you may be able to get further assistance from someone in your area who is familiar with this plan. Your Plunket nurse may be able to put you in touch with the right person, or you might get a friend to read this book and give you the moral support you need.

For a few people, this plan will not work without attention to problems in their child's daytime behaviour. Most parents find that their child's daytime behaviour improves when they get a good night's sleep. But occasionally it works the other way, and sleep problems continue until problems in daytime behaviour are also dealt with. This happens particularly with older (three years and over) children because daytime and night-time behaviours are so closely related that they cannot always be dealt with separately. There are a variety of agencies offering help in dealing with daytime problems. You could find out what help is available in your area by asking people such as your public health nurse or Plunket nurse, your local C.A.B., Psychological Services, or your G.P.

The evidence

The plan described in this book is based on experience with hundreds of families who have successfully taught their children to sleep through the night. The families came from a wide variety of backgrounds and living circumstances. Some were professionals and some were working-class people; some lived in caravans, some in flats and some had spacious homes; some had one child and some had six; some lived alone with their child, others lived in a communal situation with several families, or with several generations. They lived in noisy city streets and on peaceful country farms. They came from different racial and cultural backgrounds. The one thing they had in common was that they successfully taught their children to settle happily at bedtime and to sleep through the night.

Between 1982 and 1983 a research project was carried out to test the effectiveness of this plan. For those who are interested, the results of the research are reported in the *Australian Journal of Family Therapy* (vol. 4, no. 4). Four of the families who took part in this project have been selected as examples of people who have used the plan. The only detail that has been changed in these descriptions is the names of the children.

Mark, aged four

Mark learned to sleep through the night as a young baby, but things deteriorated when he was about eighteen months old. For no apparent reason he began waking at night, and his parents got into the habit of attending to him or letting him come into their bed, which often meant that one of the parents moved to sleep in Mark's bed. Mark got into the habit of waking every night.

Mark's parents were concerned that he was not getting enough sleep and also that their own nights were being disturbed. His Mum found that she was getting short-tempered and had problems coping during the day because of lack of sleep. His Dad had a job where he worked ten hours a day, and his Mum had a part-time job as well as taking care of Mark and his younger brother. They all needed to get a decent sleep. They sought advice on the problem from various people, and they tried giving Mark medication to help him sleep — all to no avail.

The plan to teach Mark to sleep did not get off to a good start. After following it for three nights, Mark caught a bad cold — just when he seemed to be making good progress. He had trouble breathing through his blocked nose and needed attention from his parents over the next three nights. When this was better he found that wanting to go to the toilet was a sure way to get Mum and Dad's attention when other attempts such as calling out, crying, or going to their room were not getting any response. To make matters worse, Mark's crying was waking his younger brother, who also started to get up in the night.

Finally, Mark's parents resolved that firmer action was needed. They moved his brother to another bedroom where he could not be disturbed. They closed their own bedroom door so that Mark could not keep coming in. And they put a potty in his bedroom so he could use it by himself if he needed to. Once the rules were made this clear, Mark started sleeping through the night immediately. Only once did he get up to test the situation, but when he found his parents' bedroom door closed he went back to his own room, used the potty and put himself back to sleep — all within ten minutes. He then slept through every night the following week, despite the fact that his parents began leaving their door open again. They reported that his daytime behaviour was also much improved.

During the week before his parents started teaching him to sleep, Mark's bedtime fluctuated rather wildly. Once they started using this plan, it settled down almost immediately. Similarly, the amount of time Mark was awake during the night improved dramatically once his parents resolved to take firm action on the eleventh night of the programme. Over the next seventeen nights he woke only four times: once on the twelfth night, to test the system when he found his parents' door closed, once when he was excited about his birthday, and twice when he woke briefly and settled immediately he was put back to bed.

Mark's parents were contacted several times during the following year and again three years later. Mark and his brother were once again sharing a bedroom without any problems, and Mark was continuing to sleep all night. He remembered with pride how he had learned to sleep through the night, and still talked about how he had become 'a big boy' at this time.

Ruth, aged twelve months

Unlike Mark, Ruth had never been a good sleeper before her parents tried using the sleep plan. From birth she was intolerant of animal fats and suffered from pain and constipation as a result. But even when her diet was sorted out and her health improved, Ruth remained difficult to settle and continued waking at least once every night.

To avoid bedtime battles, Ruth's parents would wait for her to get sleepy, and then give her a bottle of milk and some medication. She would finally go to sleep while feeding — some time between 8.00 p.m. and 10.30 p.m. — and be put to bed asleep. When she woke during the night she would be fed again, and one parent would stay with her until she went back to sleep.

Ruth's parents decided to teach her to sleep through the night after consulting the paediatrician, who advised that sleep problems were now just a habit. They were assured that there was no longer any medical reason why they could not leave Ruth to cry.

Her parents also visited their family doctor immediately before using the sleep plan. They were about to go away for a five-day holiday and were worried about getting enough sleep while they were away. The doctor encouraged them to go ahead with the plan to teach Ruth to sleep through the night but, in addition, gave them five days' supply of Vallergan (a children's sleeping medicine) to help them all get a much-needed rest — and in the hope that they could help Ruth break her night-waking habit.

By the fifth night Vallergan appeared to be having no effect at all. As a result of this experience, combined with the previous failure of another type of sleep medication they had tried, her parents decided not to use Vallergan again.

After they returned from their holiday, Ruth's parents commenced using the sleep plan. The main problem they had in teaching her to sleep was finding a way to keep her safely in her cot. She managed to climb out on one occasion, and on another occasion fell while attempting to get out. Her parents were advised to attach the play-pen to the sides of the cot to make it higher and completely safe.

Ruth had to learn to settle alone for two daytime sleeps and a night sleep, so she had three opportunities a day to learn the new rules. On the second night it took her an hour and a half to settle by herself, but over the first five days it was generally only five to twenty minutes before she would settle. After five nights she had learned to settle straight away by herself, and continued to do this. Similarly, it took only five nights before Ruth was sleeping through without waking.

Daytime sleeps took a little longer to organise. It was not always possible to put Ruth down for a sleep at the same time — for example, when they were out shopping — and she was at times grizzling and difficult to settle. Her parents tried putting her down for one daytime sleep in the middle of the day, but found this was not enough and went back to the old routine of two daytime sleeps. After using this plan for a week, Ruth generally settled for her morning sleep without difficulty, but every second or third day they continued to have problems getting her to settle for the afternoon sleep. This second sleep was gradually phased out over the next few months as Ruth grew older.

One of the most remarkable changes in Ruth's sleep pattern was in the amount of time she slept over each twenty-four-hour span. She began settling earlier at night — after three weeks she was settling on average over an hour earlier than she had previously — and at the same time she increased the total amount of time she slept by two-and-a-half hours, to thirteen hours fifty minutes per day. Along with her parents' comment that she was now 'a much more enjoyable and manageable little girl', this clearly demonstrated that she had not been getting nearly as much sleep as she needed before they decided to put the sleep plan into action.

Over the next few months, Ruth's sleep pattern fluctuated as she suffered first from an inner-ear infection, and later from dysentery and vomiting. At these times she needed her parents' attention at night, and quickly got back into the habit of night-waking. Once she recovered, her parents were able to teach her to sleep through again without any problems. When they were contacted six months later, Ruth's parents reported that she was now sleeping through every night, and that she had moved from her cot to a bed quite happily.

Joanne, aged fifteen months

Joanne's mother was a single parent who still lived in the family home with her own parents, her brother, sister, and her sister's boyfriend. Consequently, there were six adults in the household who had to co-operate to teach Joanne to sleep through the night. Joanne's mother and aunt were particularly involved as they shared a bedroom with her.

Joanne had never been a good sleeper. She had no particular bedtime, and was put to sleep whenever she looked tired. She was given a bottle to suck on in her cot until she drifted off to sleep, and tended to wake once or twice during the night. At these times she was given an empty bottle for comfort, and was sometimes allowed into her mother's bed. Her mother had also tried growling at her, rocking her back to sleep, and three different kinds of medication. During the day Joanne had one or two sleeps when she settled with a bottle — or if the family was out she often fell asleep in the car.

The first time Joanne was put to bed without a bottle it took her twenty minutes to settle. The next day she took only two minutes to settle — for each of her daytime sleeps as well as her night-time sleep. Within three days she was settling straight away. Similarly, she learned to sleep through the night very quickly. On the first night she woke four times for a total of an hour. The second night she woke once and stayed awake for forty-five minutes. The third and fourth nights she slept through, something she'd very rarely done before. Over the next week she slept through every second night, waking one night for two minutes, one night for five, and two nights when she really tested the new rules for one and one-and-a-quarter hours respectively. Within a month she was settling almost immediately every night and sleeping through six or seven nights a week. Her mother found her easier to manage during the day, and the whole family was pleased.

When the family was contacted a month later, Joanne had been ill and was back to waking once or twice every night. Her mother was encouraged to put the sleep plan into action once again when Joanne was better, and she managed to do this without any difficulty. A final check with the family six months later revealed that Joanne was settling easily and sleeping through almost every night. Her mother felt good and reported that Joanne was much happier now that she was getting uninterrupted sleep.

Grant, aged two years

Grant had learned to settle by himself when he was quite small, but this was disrupted when he had pneumonia at seven months. However, he had always woken at some stage during the night after settling.

When his parents sought help with Grant's sleep, he had no regular bedtime and was usually put to bed after being nursed asleep. He woke two or three times every night and was breast-fed until he went back to sleep. His mother wanted to wean him but was finding this difficult.

The first night Grant was put to bed awake he cried for seventy minutes before finally falling asleep — on the floor behind the bedroom door. He woke three times in the night, once for an hour, once for twenty minutes, and once for five minutes — although he didn't cry all this time. Twice he went into the lounge and tried to go to sleep there, and several times he went into his parents' room and had to be returned to his own bed. Once he fell asleep under his bed. This was a difficult night for the whole family, but it gave Grant's parents several opportunities to show him that they were serious about the new rules, and this made it easier for Grant in the long run.

The second night it took Grant an hour to settle, but he woke only once — for five minutes. The third night he settled within twenty-five minutes, but later in the night he did manage to sneak into his parents' bed and go to sleep before they found him and returned him to his own bed. On the fifth night he slept through and, with a few exceptions, continued to do so for the rest of the month.

It took two and a half weeks before Grant learned to settle happily by himself when first put to bed. On a few occasions his parents' resolution faltered and they lay with him before he went to sleep or fed him when he was upset. Unfortunately, this meant that the rules weren't so clear for Grant, and they realised that it was confusing him. His mother decided to breast-feed only after breakfast and after dinner — not when he was upset — and they stopped lying with him at bedtime. Gradually Grant learned to settle by himself over shorter periods until finally he was settling almost immediately — both daytime and night-time.

Records kept by Grant's parents demonstrate that he was getting more than two hours extra sleep a day within a month of using this plan. He was settling much earlier at night and awake much less during the night. Clearly, he had not been getting as much sleep as he needed. His parents reported that he was a 'totally different boy' after he'd had a good night's sleep.

Three months later Grant's sleep pattern was interrupted when he spent several days in hospital with suspected meningitis. For a while he was waking twice a night, sometimes wetting the bed and calling out for his parents. While he was ill they attended to him and let him into their bed for comfort, but once he had fully recovered they were able to get him back into the good sleep habits he had previously learned.

Now, three years later, Grant is at school and continues to sleep well. In fact, his mother reports that 'it would take a thunderbolt to wake him'. She recalls that she found it difficult to put the sleep plan into action, but she also sees it as a tremendous learning experience — and one they were able to make the most of when it came to preventing sleep problems with the new baby.